JOURNEY 101
STEPS TO THE LIFE GOD INTENDS

KNOWING GOD

Participant Guide

JOURNEY 101
STEPS TO THE LIFE GOD INTENDS

This three-part basic faith course is designed to teach what it means to know, love, and serve God. Each of the three separate, interactive six-week studies uses a group teaching format, combining video teaching and small group table breakouts. The three studies include:

KNOWING GOD. Explore the good news of the Bible and discover Bible study tools and resources to deepen your understanding of God and the Scriptures.

LOVING GOD. Experience spiritual transformation through spiritual practices that will help you fall more in love with God and grow in your relationship with God and others.

SERVING GOD. Understand the biblical context for service that will enable you to use your hands, your time, and your spiritual gifts to serve others and share Christ.

COMPONENTS:

Participant Guide (1 for each study)—Six interactive session guides with space for responding to questions and activities and recording personal reflections.

Leader Guide (1 for each study)—Six complete session guides for facilitating a group with additional leader helps.

Daily Readings—Serves as the devotional companion for the entire three-part Journey 101 series. Ninety devotions (thirty devotions per study).

DVD—Three-disc set (120 minutes per DVD/study; 360 minutes total)

Preview Book—Provides an overview of the topics covered in the entire three-part Journey 101 course.

Leader Kit—One each of the components listed above.

KNOWING GOD

PARTICIPANT GUIDE

Carol Cartmill

Jeff Kirby

Michelle Kirby

Abingdon Press

Nashville

JOURNEY 101: KNOWING GOD
PARTICIPANT GUIDE

This book is printed on acid-free paper.

ISBN 978-1-4267-6574-2

13 14 15 16 17 18 19 20 21 22—10 9 8 7 6 5 4 3 2 1

MANUFACTURED IN THE UNITED STATES OF AMERICA

Projects like this are never created in a vacuum. The work represented here is built on five years of offering this course to the members of our home church. We would like to recognize the contributions of so many at The United Methodist Church of the Resurrection who helped to lead, facilitate, and shape this study, especially: Jonathan Bell, Susan Campbell, Nicole Conard, Gia Garey-Moser, Darren Lippe, Debi Nixon, David Robertson, Chuck Russell, and Clayton Smith. We dedicate this study to them.

CONTENTS

Introduction

THE JOURNEY

When we give our lives to Jesus Christ and commit to follow him, we embark on a lifelong journey of knowing, loving, and serving God. Growing as a Christian and becoming a committed follower of Jesus Christ means . . .

> **knowing God** by becoming theologically informed,
> **loving God** and experiencing spiritual transformation, and
> **serving God** by using our hands to serve others and share Christ.

Journey 101 is a three-part course designed to help guide us on this journey of knowing, loving, and serving God. As we embark on this journey, it is vitally important that we know the destination, the place where we want to end up. And that destination is to become deeply committed Christians—people who know, love, and serve God with increasing passion and dedication. As we journey toward this destination, the studies in this series will help us to answer some important questions:

- How does a deeply committed Christian grow to know God more deeply?

- How would our lives be transformed if we loved God with the fullness of our hearts?

- How should we, as deeply committed Christians, be serving in the world?

To help us know that we are on the right track to our destination, we have identified fifteen markers to guide us along the way. We call these markers the fifteen core traits of a deeply committed Christian; these traits paint a picture of what it looks like to live as a deeply committed follower of Jesus Christ. Each study in the Journey 101 series focuses on five of these core traits. (See pages 12-13 for detailed descriptions of these core traits.)

Because starting any journey can sometimes be daunting, particularly if you find yourself in unfamiliar territory or surroundings, Journey 101 serves as a navigation system that provides directions, routes, and traveling companions to support and encourage you along the way. Here is what you can expect to learn in each of the three studies:

KNOWING GOD

- Gain a better understanding of the essentials of the Christian faith.
- Experience new Bible study tools and resources.
- Discover more about the church.
- Discuss ethics and our Christian response to life's decisions.
- Understand more about God's will for your life.

LOVING GOD

- Learn about the Holy Spirit's transforming power in our lives.
- Understand more about what it means to love God with all your heart, soul, mind, and strength and to love your neighbor as you love yourself (Luke 10:27).
- Understand and experience key spiritual practices including Bible study, prayer, worship, fasting, guidance, and journaling.
- Learn to recognize the "fruit" of God's transforming activity in our lives—love, joy, peace, patience, kindness, generosity, gentleness, faithfulness, and self-control.

SERVING GOD

- Focus on the Bible's concern for the poor and for justice, while learning how to be instruments of God's love in a broken, hurting world.
- Learn how to share the good news of Jesus in loving, winsome, and non-judgmental ways.

- Understand spiritual gifts and talents and how to use those gifts to bless others and build up the body of Christ.

- Learn how our money and material possessions are not a measure of success or a means of self-gratification, but a resource to responsibly use to glorify God.

- View time as a gift from God, to be used in keeping with God's purposes, avoiding compulsive busyness and submitting our calendars to God's guiding and control.

Although it is recommended that you take each of these studies, there is no set order in which you must complete them.

WHAT TO EXPECT

Journey 101 is designed as an in-class experience. In other words, everything takes place in the group setting. There is no homework to be done outside of class. This participant guide serves as your "map" for the weekly group experience. You will need to bring it with you to each class, along with a pen or pencil and a Bible. (If you forget your Bible or don't own one, there will be extras available.)

Each week you will spend time connecting with those in your group, reflecting on where you are on your journey, viewing and discussing several video segments, reviewing what you have learned, and praying together. Simply follow along in your participant guide as your leader guides you through the session. Questions and activities that you are to answer or complete in your book are highlighted in bold type. Share your answers to the discussion questions as a group, taking notes in your participant guide as you move through the questions together. Whether you write a little or a lot, your participant guide will become your own personal record of your journey and the insights you gain along the way.

Though no homework is involved, you may wish to use the devotional companion, *Journey 101 Daily Readings*, in your private devotions while completing the three-part Journey 101 series. These devotions will help to enrich your understanding and application of what you are learning in class.

We believe that nothing in the world will bring you greater joy, greater challenge, and greater meaning than the journey into life as God intended us to live it. As you begin the journey, open yourself to what God has to teach you through the Scriptures, prayer, and the guidance of the Holy Spirit.

FIFTEEN CORE TRAITS OF A DEEPLY COMMITTED CHRISTIAN

KNOWING GOD

Christian Essentials—Deeply committed Christians understand the essential gospel on which most Christians agree, across denominational lines and centuries, expressed in historic creeds such as the Apostles' and Nicene creeds, and can share the gospel intelligently with non-Christian friends.

Bible Understanding—Deeply committed Christians know the grand sweep of the Bible's story of salvation, including a basic timeline of biblical events. They understand the divine/human nature of the Bible and know how to read it, not merely as an ancient document or a reference book of spiritual answers, but for personal spiritual growth.

Church/Denomination—Deeply committed Christians value the church as the body of Christ, God's people journeying in community, and know the teachings characteristic of their particular denomination.

Basic Christian Ethics—Deeply committed Christians understand how to apply their Christian faith to important ethical issues and are committed to living out Christian ethical principles such as justice, integrity, peace, and responsibility for the well-being of others.

Knowing God's Will—Deeply committed Christians know the broad scope of God's purpose for human beings, and have a growing sense of how to discern God's will for their lives through prayer, Bible study, and the wisdom of other Christians.

LOVING GOD

Surrender—Deeply committed Christians surrender the control of every aspect of their lives to Jesus, repent of sin, set aside their own desires and sense of importance, and offer their lives in obedient service to God.

Transformation—Deeply committed Christians are being continually transformed by the power of the Holy Spirit, and sense that power molding their values, priorities, and relationships into more Christ-like patterns.

Spiritual Disciplines—Deeply committed Christians practice various spiritual disciplines (for example, prayer, Bible reading, worship, solitude, meditation, fasting) as a means of surrendering to Jesus and opening their lives to the Holy Spirit's transforming activity.

Fruit of the Spirit—Deeply committed Christians are continually growing in the inner qualities and outward actions identified as "the fruit of the Spirit" in Galatians 5:22-23: "love, joy, peace, patience, kindness, goodness, faithfulness, gentleness, and self-control."

Authentic Community—Deeply committed Christians share their faith journeys with groups of Christian friends in mutual encouragement and accountability, developing spiritual honesty and trust through sharing and support.

SERVING GOD

Service to others—Deeply committed Christians are instruments of God's love in a broken, hurting world, living lives of service to others with a strong (though not exclusive) focus on the Bible's concern for the poor and for justice.

Sharing Christ—Deeply committed Christians are eager to share the good news of Jesus in loving, winsome, and non-judgmental ways, and are ready to "give an answer to everyone who asks you to give the reason for the hope that you have" (1 Peter 3:15).

Spiritual Gifts/Talents—Deeply committed Christians understand clearly with "sober judgment" (Romans 12:3) which spiritual gifts and talents they have and use those gifts to bless others and build up the body of Christ.

Financial Gifts—Deeply committed Christians view money and material possessions not as a measure of success or as a means of self-gratification, but as a resource for whose use they are responsible to God, and they submit their financial lives to God's guiding and control.

Time—Deeply committed Christians see time as a gift from God to be used in keeping with God's purposes, avoid compulsive busyness, and submit their calendars to God's guiding and control.

RECEIVING CHRIST

This is what the LORD says:
"Let not the wise boast of their wisdom
or the strong boast of their strength
or the rich boast of their riches,
but let the one who boasts boast about this:
that they have the understanding to know me,
that I am the LORD, who exercises kindness,
justice and righteousness on earth, for in these I delight,"
declares the LORD.

Jeremiah 9:23-24

CORE TRAITS

- Christian Essentials
- Knowing God's Will

WELCOME

Welcome to Journey 101: Knowing God. Our prayer for you is that through this study and through your conversation you will come to know God more fully and discover who you are in God. In this session you will hear about what it means to know and be known by God, wrestle with the problem of sin, and experience the joy and freedom that come from receiving Christ. Open your mind and heart; let God speak to you right here, right now as we gather in God's name.

CONNECT

Discuss the following questions with your group to get to know one another better and get the conversation started.

- Take a few minutes to introduce yourself. Share why you are interested in taking this class.

- Describe a favorite gift you received as a child and why it was special.

- If you could choose, would you rather be an excellent athlete, artist, or musician? Why?

- Who has most inspired you personally and why?

- What life experience has strengthened you the most?

In the space that follows, write the names of people you have met in your group and one thing about each of them that you learned in conversation. This will help you remember names and get to know one another a little more.

REFLECT

Here, at the beginning of your study, assess your understanding of what it means to know God, and let your thoughts be a landmark for your journey. Take a few moments to write what comes to mind when you think about knowing God.

For me, knowing God means . . .

1 VIDEO HIGHLIGHTS: A RELATIONSHIP WITH GOD

This is what the Lord says:
  "Let not the wise boast of their wisdom
    or the strong boast of their strength
    or the rich boast of their riches,
  but let the one who boasts boast about this:
    that they have the understanding to know me,
  that I am the Lord, who exercises kindness,
  justice and righteousness on earth,
  for in these I delight,"
    declares the Lord.
                    Jeremiah 9:23-24

- God is and always will be above our comprehension. Yet the amazing thing is that we can know God, and we can know God personally.

  Great is the Lord and most worthy of praise;
    his greatness no one can fathom.
                    Psalm 145:3

- At the heart of the Christian faith is a *relationship* with God.

  ○ We are dependent on God revealing himself to us.

  The heavens declare the glory of God;
    the skies proclaim the work of his hands.
                    Psalm 19:1

  ○ Our most intimate knowledge of God comes to us through the person of Jesus Christ.

- We were created by God to know and experience his love, presence, and power in our lives.

- God did not create us because God was in need. God enjoyed perfect love and fellowship within the Trinity.

- God created us to share in his glory and enjoy relationship.

  "Bring my sons from afar
    and my daughters from the ends of the earth—
  everyone who is called by my name,
    whom I created for my glory,
    whom I formed and made."
                    Isaiah 43:6b-7

- God has created us to know, love, and serve God.

1 GROUP DISCUSSION

1. Describe how your journey to know God began. When did *God* become more than just a word for you?

2. Have someone read Genesis 2:7 aloud. How might this Scripture give insight to your understanding of the type of relationship God intended to have with humankind?

3. Have someone read John 1:9-13 and Ephesians 2:8-9 aloud. What clues do these verses give us about our relationship with God and God's desire to be known by us?

4. Have someone read Genesis 1:26-30; 3:8 aloud. In the space below, write the verses in your own words. What do they tell you about why we were created?

5. Have someone read John 15:4-5 aloud. What is the role of Jesus and what is the role of his followers according to these verses? In your opinion, how does this passage apply to this week's lesson?

2 VIDEO HIGHLIGHTS: THE PROBLEM OF SIN

The woman saw that the tree was beautiful with delicious food and that the tree would provide wisdom, so she took some of its fruit and ate it, and also gave some to her husband, who was with her, and he ate it. Then they both saw clearly and knew that they were naked. So they sewed fig leaves together and made garments for themselves.

During that day's cool evening breeze, they heard the sound of the LORD God walking in the garden; and the man and his wife hid themselves from the LORD God in the middle of the garden's trees.
The LORD God called to the man and said to him, "Where are you?"
The man replied, "I heard your sound in the garden; I was afraid because I was naked, and I hid myself."
He said, "Who told you that you were naked? Did you eat from the tree, which I commanded you not to eat?"
The man said, "The woman you gave me, she gave me some fruit from the tree, and I ate."
The LORD God said to the woman, "What have you done?!"
Genesis 3:6-13a CEB

- Sin is the severing of our relationship with God.

  Sin is the despairing refusal to find your deepest identity in your relationship and service to God. Sin is seeking to become oneself, to get an identity, apart from God.[1]
  —Timothy Keller

- The first of the Ten Commandments is to have no other gods before the one true God.

- Sin is more than doing bad things; it also can be having good things that become of ultimate importance in our lives.

- Jesus taught in spiritual stories we call parables. Parables are stories that Jesus created in order to teach an essential spiritual truth. One of the most beloved parables is the one we call the Prodigal Son. It can be found in Luke 15.

- The word *repent* might be explained as coming to our senses.

  "How many of my father's hired men have food to spare, and here I am starving to death!"
  Luke 15:17

- Life with God must be better than the life I have created apart from God.

- The great Saint Augustine once wrote, "Our lives are not ordered properly and our hearts are restless until they find their rest in Thee!"[2]

- All of us have sinned and fall short of the glory of God. (See Romans 3:23.)

- Sin is like a disease, and we've all got it. But there is good news. The word *gospel* means good news, and the good news of the Christian message is that God has come to help us.

2 GROUP DISCUSSION

1. Have someone read Genesis 3:1-15 aloud. How is sin exposed in these verses?

2. Who did the woman blame the sin on?

3. Who did the man blame the sin on?

4. Whose fault is the sin? Why?

5. Have someone read Luke 15:11-24 aloud. What is the sin in this story?

6. What is the father's response to the sin?

7. How do we sin by making "good things have ultimate importance in our lives"?

3 VIDEO HIGHLIGHTS: THE ANSWER TO SIN

"For even the Son of Man did not come to be served, but to serve, and to give his life as a ransom for many."
Mark 10:45

- Jesus Christ is God's answer to the problem of sin.

> *He was despised and rejected by men,*
> *   a man of sorrows, and familiar with suffering.*
> *Like one from whom men hide their faces*
> *   he was despised, and we esteemed him not.*
> *Surely he took up our infirmities*
> *   and carried our sorrows,*
> *yet we considered him stricken by God,*
> *   smitten by him, and afflicted.*
> *But he was pierced for our transgressions,*
> *   he was crushed for our iniquities;*
> *the punishment that brought us peace was upon him,*
> *   and by his wounds we are healed.*
> Isaiah 53:3-5

- God was motivated by love to send God's only Son to bear the sins of the world.

> *"For God so loved the world that he gave his one and only Son, that whoever believes in him shall not perish but would have eternal life."*
> John 3:16

- God has come to bear the punishment for our selfishness and sin.

- The good news requires a response.

> *"God extends to us an invitation of grace, and each of us must choose to respond personally to this invitation."*

Are you confident that you are a Christian?

- We can know God personally by receiving Christ into our lives.

Dear Lord Jesus,

*   I come before you in honesty and in humility. I confess that I have sinned before you and am in need of your grace and forgiveness. Jesus, I pray that you would come into my life. I want to be a Christian. Please give me the gift of your Holy Spirit. Help me turn away from all the things that turn me away from you. I offer you my life. Empower me by your Holy Spirit to experience your wonderful love and grace. Give me the grace and the courage to follow you and to discover*

what you would have me do and be as I seek to glorify you with my life. Thank you for coming in. In your holy name. Amen.

3 GROUP DISCUSSION

1. Maybe you've been a Christian as long as you can remember, maybe you accepted Christ when you were a teen or young adult, maybe you just prayed the prayer a few minutes ago, or perhaps you are still undecided. If you have accepted Christ, share about your experience.

2. What was Jesus' ultimate mission during his earthly life?

3. Why did God send Jesus to save us from our sins? (Refer to John 3:16.)

4. What does the good news require?

5. Before you came here today, what did you imagine it took to become a Christian?

6. How would you describe your understanding now of why Jesus came to earth and how we can receive him into our lives?

REVIEW

In this session, the three main points were:

1.

2.

3.

What is God's answer to the problem of sin?

How do we participate in that saving work?

Closing

On the last video segment you heard a story about how a seventy-three-year-old retired executive came to receive Christ personally and discovered that it is never too late to begin a new life through Jesus Christ. In three sentences, how would you begin to describe *your* God story? Think about it like this: Before Christ, Choose Christ, Live for Christ. Use the following questions to begin to shape your story. You might be able to complete one, two, or all three questions. Answer the questions and then share with your group.

1. **What was life like before you met Jesus Christ?**

2. **What was the tipping point that led you to choose and receive Christ?**

3. **What does your life look like now that you know God through the gift of Jesus Christ and are living for him?**

PRAY TOGETHER

Share joys and concerns among your group. Write down anything you are asked to pray for.

Eternal God, you call us to be in relationship with you. From the beginning of time you have been a God of relationship. You formed us to need you and to need one another. Today, Lord, we pray that you would open our hearts to know you more. We invite Jesus Christ to live in us, forgive us of our sins, and lead us on this journey to know you more and more. Amen.

WALKING IT OUT

- Continue the journey by reflecting on the three main ideas of the session throughout the coming week:

  1. We were created to be in relationship with God, to know God, and to be known by God.

  2. Sin separated us from the union that God intended.

  3. Jesus Christ is God's answer to the problem of sin.

- In your personal prayer time,

  - give thanks that God desires to be in relationship with you. Tell God that you want to know God more.

  - acknowledge that sin has separated all of us from the union that God intended.

  - praise God for sending Jesus Christ to be the answer to the problem of sin—not only sin in general but also and specifically *your* sins. Accept God's grace and mercy.

- Give more thought to your God story (Before Christ/Choose Christ/Live for Christ). Ask God to begin giving you opportunities to share your God story with others. Watch for opportunities to tell others about the ways that being in relationship with God makes a difference in your life.

- Spend time each day in personal devotion and prayer. You may want to use the *Journey 101 Daily Readings* as a tool to guide your time with God.

COMPREHENDING CHRIST'S TEACHINGS

Again Jesus began to teach by the lake. The crowd that gathered around him was so large that he got into a boat and sat in it out on the lake, while all the people were along the shore at the water's edge. He taught them many things by parables, and in his teaching said: "Listen! A farmer went out to sow his seed."

Mark 4:1-3

CORE TRAITS

- Christian Essentials
- Bible Knowledge

WELCOME

We grow in knowledge of God by studying the words of Jesus Christ and seeking to incorporate them into our lives. The teachings of Jesus are revolutionary and require careful and thoughtful study. In this session, you are invited to dive into Jesus' teachings and seek understanding of what they are all about. God bless you as you explore the Scriptures today.

CONNECT

Discuss the following questions with your group to get to know one another better and get the conversation started.

- Would you stop eating all junk food in order to live five years longer?

- Where did you grow up?

- Would you rather meet your great-grandparents or your great-grandchildren?

- Who was the best teacher you ever had in school? What made him or her so effective?

- Last week we discussed the fact that God created you for a wonderful purpose—to know, love, and serve God. What is one thing you learned or took away from the lesson?

In the space that follows, write the names of people in your group and one thing about each of them that you learned in conversation. This will help you remember names and get to know one another a little more.

REFLECT

Consider what you know about Jesus' teachings. Write a few reflections about your current understanding of what Jesus taught and preached in his time on earth.

My understanding of Christ's teachings is . . .

1 | VIDEO HIGHLIGHTS: ESSENTIALS FOR READING SCRIPTURE

Again Jesus began to teach by the lake. The crowd that gathered around him was so large that he got into a boat and sat in it out on the lake, while all the people were along the shore at the water's edge. He taught them many things by parables, and in his teaching said: "Listen! A farmer went out to sow his seed."

Mark 4:1-3

- Jesus is the greatest teacher of all time.

- We come to know God by understanding the teachings of Jesus.

- The teachings of Jesus are revolutionary and require careful and thoughtful study.

- The context of the story determines what we hear. We understand the story's meaning based on the storyline *in its environment*.

- We must interpret Scripture in light of its context.

- When we study the Bible, there are three essential questions:

  1. What did this passage mean to the people who wrote it?

  2. What did it mean to those who first heard or read it?

  3. In view of these first two questions, what does it mean to me personally?

- Jesus' teachings must be understood within the greater story of God's rescue operation of the world through Israel.

1 | GROUP DISCUSSION

1. **When you sit down to read the Bible, what approach do you take as you read?**

2. Have someone read aloud Mark 4:1-3. What do these verses say about Jesus' teaching style?

3. Why is context so important for understanding and comprehension?

4. When have you been misunderstood or when have you misunderstood someone or something because of a lack of context?

2	**VIDEO HIGHLIGHTS: THE TEACHING MINISTRY OF JESUS**

When Jesus had finished saying these things, the crowds were amazed at his teaching, because he taught as one who had authority, and not as their teachers of the law.
Matthew 7:28-29

1. Jesus' teachings had unique authority.

Now some teachers of the law were sitting there, thinking to themselves, "Why does this fellow talk like that? He's blaspheming! Who can forgive sins but God alone?"

Immediately Jesus knew in his spirit that this was what they were thinking in their hearts, and he said to them, "Why are you thinking these things? Which is easier: to say to this paralyzed man, 'Your sins are forgiven,' or to say, 'Get up, take your mat and walk'? But I want you to know that the Son of Man has authority on earth to forgive sins." So he said to the man, "I tell you, get up, take your mat and go home." He got up, took his mat and walked out in full view of them all. This amazed everyone and they praised God, saying, "We have never seen anything like this!"
Mark 2:6-12

- Jesus had an open-hand approach to teaching, not a heavy hand.

2. Jesus' teachings were rooted in the old but also were creative and new.

29

- When Jesus repeated the phrase "You have heard that it was said, but I say to you . . ." he was helping people understand what they already knew while opening up the meaning.

3. Jesus spoke in graphic word pictures including parables, paradoxes, and epigrams.

   - Parables—short stories that use familiar situations to communicate truth.

   - Paradoxes—statements that seem contradictory but express a truth: We reign by serving. We are exalted when we are humbled. We are strong when we are weak.

   - Epigrams—short, witty sayings used to teach.

4. Jesus' teachings made people think for themselves and elicited a decision.

   After calling the crowd together with his disciples, Jesus said to them, "All who want to come after me must say no to themselves, take up their cross, and follow me. All who want to save their lives will lose them. But all who lose their lives because of me and because of the good news will save them. Why would people gain the whole world but lose their lives? What will people give in exchange for their lives?
   Mark 8:34-37 CEB

5. Jesus' teachings were motivated by love. He genuinely loved people. He taught because he dearly loved people.

   One catches the spark of love from one who loves.[1]
   —Saint Augustine

   - Jesus' love shows us what it is like to know God.

   - Jesus' teachings were understood as good news for sinners.

2 | GROUP DISCUSSION

1. What do you find compelling about the teaching ministry of Jesus?

2. Have someone read aloud Mark 2:6-12. Why were the people so amazed?

3. When has someone "opened up the meaning" for you, either in the Scriptures or in life lessons?

4. According to *Nelson's New Illustrated Bible Dictionary*, a *parable* is defined as "a short simple story designed to communicate a spiritual truth, religious principle, or moral lesson; a figure of speech in which truth is illustrated by a comparison or example drawn from everyday experiences."[2] Why do you think Jesus so often spoke in parables?

5. Have someone read aloud Mark 8:34-37. What is the decision that Jesus is inviting his hearers (and us) to make?

6. What was Jesus' primary motivation as he taught? How do his teachings illustrate this?

7. Why is the deep love of Jesus good news for us?

3 VIDEO HIGHLIGHTS: THE KINGDOM OF GOD

The LORD will rule forever and always.
Exodus 15:18 CEB

- The "kingdom of God" means God's dynamic reign and rule over the heavens and the earth.

- When Jesus taught, he almost always spoke about the kingdom of God. He transformed the common understandings about the kingdom of God:

1. The Kingdom was central to Israel's expectations.

   - When God's kingdom did arrive, it would be characterized by:

     ○ the return of the people of Israel from exile,

     ○ the defeat of all of Israel's enemies,

     ○ the rebuilding and reestablishment of the Temple in Jerusalem.

2. Jesus taught that the Kingdom was both present and future—both here now and yet to come.

   - Ancient prophets of Israel anticipated a future day when God would dramatically enter human history to make right all that was wrong. They called this "The Day of the Lord." This day would separate the present age and the future.

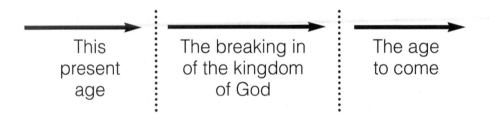

| This present age | The breaking in of the kingdom of God | The age to come |

   - Old Testament prophecies pointing to Jesus:

     ○ Jesus came to rescue humanity. (Isaiah 58:6; 61:1-2)

     ○ Jesus was in the line of David. (Jeremiah 23:5)

     ○ Jesus was anointed by John the Baptist. (Isaiah 40:3; Malachi 3:1)

     ○ Jesus received the Spirit of God and was announced as God's own Son. (Isaiah 11:2; Psalm 2:7)

     ○ Jesus' ministry was a demonstration of the power of God's Spirit. (Isaiah 40:10)

     ○ Jesus was acclaimed by his people in the triumphal entry into Jerusalem. (Psalm 118:26)

   - Jesus was unlike earthly kings in that his crown was made of thorns and his throne was a cross.

3. The parables concerning the Kingdom were central teachings of Jesus:

- The parables were not generalized stories or fables; they were created by Jesus to communicate an essential and spiritual truth related to the in-breaking of the rule and reign of God's kingdom.

- The parables redefined expectations of how the kingdom of God would come to be known.

- Jesus taught in such a fashion that challenged people to think and understand in new ways, make choices for themselves, and feel loved in a very personal and passionate way by this very unique and special teacher. His teachings challenge us in the same ways today.

3 GROUP DISCUSSION

1. Have someone read aloud Matthew 6:33. What do you think Jesus meant when he said, "Seek first his kingdom and his righteousness"?

2. Where in your life do you need to seek God "first"?

3. What prevents us from seeking God first in all things?

4. How did the Old Testament prophecies mentioned above point to Jesus?

5. Have someone read aloud the parable of the sower found in Mark 4:1-20, and complete the chart below.

The Parable of the Sower
Mark 4:1-20

Sower scatters ___Seed___

Sower scatters ___God's Message___

Type of Soil	Results	Jesus' Interpretation
Shallow	Wilted Shallow roots	Hear but roots shallow
Thorns	Choked	Message crowded out by life
Fertile	Produced crop	Hear & accept
Wayside Base ground	birds ate	Here don't accept Harvest

Parable as told to crowd

Parable as told to disciples

6. Have someone read aloud the parable of the mustard seed found in Mark 4:30-32. What does this parable add to our understanding of the kingdom of God?

REVIEW

In this session, the main points were:
1.

2.

3.

4.

5.

6.

What is unique about Jesus' teachings compared to teachers the people would have previously heard, and even teachers today?

Why is it so important to really comprehend the teachings of Jesus?

CLOSING

In the last video segment you heard about how looking closely at the teachings of Jesus transformed Justin's life in amazing ways. Think about how you might be intentional about digging in to Jesus' teachings. Discuss some ways to incorporate Bible reading into your daily or weekly schedule.

Use the calendar below to map out an average week in your life. Then look for some holes in your schedule where you might squeeze in fifteen minutes to study Jesus' teachings.

	Mon.	Tues.	Wed.	Thurs.	Fri.
5 A.M.					
6					
7					
8					
9					
10					
11					
12 P.M.					
1					
2					
3					
4					
5					
6					
7					
8					
9					
10					
11					

PRAY TOGETHER

Share joys and concerns among your group. Write down anything you are asked to pray for.

Lord God, we are so thankful for the great and amazing teachings of Jesus. Help us to comprehend your message for us and allow your love to penetrate our hearts so that we can grow in the knowledge of you and of others. In Christ's name. Amen.

WALKING IT OUT

- Continue the journey by reflecting on the main ideas of the session throughout the coming week:

    1. Jesus' teachings had unique authority.

    2. Jesus' teachings were rooted in the old but also were creative and new.

    3. Jesus used great word pictures to help people comprehend his teachings.

    4. Jesus made people think for themselves.

    5. Jesus' teachings were motivated by love.

    6. Jesus' teachings were primarily about the kingdom of God.

- In your personal prayer time,

    ○ give thanks that God sent Jesus to save us and to teach us how to know the Father,

    ○ invite God to illuminate Jesus' teachings and give you new insight as you dig into the teachings of Jesus, and

    ○ offer praise for God's witness of love and grace in the Bible.

- As you commit to studying the Bible, commit verses to memory and ask God to give you opportunities to bless people with them.

- Give more thought to your own unique God story (Before Christ/Choose Christ/Live for Christ; page 23). Continue looking for opportunities to share your God story with others.

LEARNING THE SCRIPTURES

*All Scripture is God-breathed and is useful for teaching, rebuking,
correcting and training in righteousness, so that the man of God may
be thoroughly equipped for every good work.*
2 Timothy 3:16-17

CORE TRAITS

- Bible Understanding
- Church/Denomination
- Knowing God's Will

WELCOME

The Jewish and Christian faiths teach that God has revealed himself in historical acts and people. For the Christian, this revelation reaches its climax in the sending of God's Son, the historical Jesus. In this session you will discover that the Bible is the divinely inspired record of those saving events and is itself part of the divine self-disclosure. Invite God to help you understand and come to love the Word of God so that you may grow in faith and know God more fully.

CONNECT

Discuss the following questions with your group to get to know one another better and get the conversation started.

- Can you think of a fashion trend you wore that was very cool at the time but now looks ridiculous?

- Which historical sporting event would you most like to have witnessed?

- Which would you prefer: a quiet, safe life or an uncertain life of great adventure? Why?

- Which do you think is more important to possess, common sense or intelligence? Why?

- Last week we discussed Knowing God through the teachings of Jesus Christ. What is one thing you learned or took away from the lesson?

In the space that follows, write down the names of people in your group and one thing about each of them that you learned in conversation. This will help you remember names and get to know one another a little more.

REFLECT

Consider what you know about the Bible. Would you say you have a

_____ **nonexistent understanding of the Scriptures?**
_____ **a working knowledge of the Scriptures?**
_____ **a pretty good grasp of the Scriptures?**

Write down the names of a few Bible characters or stories that come to mind:

1   VIDEO HIGHLIGHTS: AN OVERVIEW OF THE BIBLE

*[The Bible is] a big book, full of big stories with big characters.
They have big ideas (not least about themselves) and they make big
mistakes. It's about God and greed and grace; about life, lust, laugh-
ter, and loneliness. It's about birth, beginnings, and betrayal; about
siblings, squabbles, and sex; about power and prayer and prison and
passion.*

And that's only Genesis.[1]

—N. T. Wright

- The Bible is the Word of God in the words of people.

- The Bible was written by more than forty different people during the
  course of approximately fifteen hundred years.

- The Bible has two major sections:

  - Old Testament: Recounts the story of God's people prior to Jesus'
    life

  - New Testament: Chronicles the coming of Christ and the first forty
    years or so of the Christian movement

Old Testament

The word *testament* also can be translated as "covenant." The term "Old
Testament," therefore, refers first to God's covenant or promise to bless humankind through the Jewish nation. The Scriptures of the Old Testament record the
story of God's chosen people, Israel, and their relationship to his covenant to
bless all nations through them.

The Old Testament Bookshelf (5-12-5-5-12) is a way to depict the number
of books in each division:

> law (5)
> history (12)
> poetry and wisdom (5)
> major prophets (5)
> minor prophets (12)

The Books of Law (Torah)

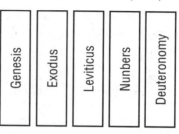

Genesis | Exodus | Leviticus | Numbers | Deuteronomy

From creation to covenant / laws, census, and journey to the promised land

The Books of History

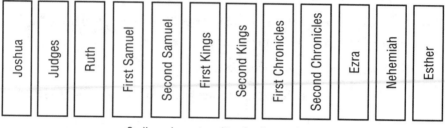

Joshua | Judges | Ruth | First Samuel | Second Samuel | First Kings | Second Kings | First Chronicles | Second Chronicles | Ezra | Nehemiah | Esther

God's saving acts written by the prophets

Wisdom and Poetry (various contributors)

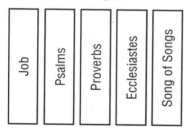

Job | Psalms | Proverbs | Ecclesiastes | Song of Songs

Explorations of life's important questions through story, poetry, songs, and sayings

Major Prophets

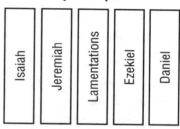

Isaiah | Jeremiah | Lamentations | Ezekiel | Daniel

Conveyed messages of God to the people of Israel

Minor Prophets

Hosea | Joel | Amos | Obadiah | Jonah | Micah | Nahum | Habakkuk | Zephaniah | Haggai | Zachariah | Malachi

Conveyed messages of God to the people of Israel

New Testamant

The term "New Testament" refers first to the covenant God made with all people to save them through God's Son, Jesus Christ. The Scriptures of the New Testament show how God's Old Covenant is fulfilled in Jesus Christ. It describes how the early Christians became the church, and how we are to live in the light of the risen presence of Christ.

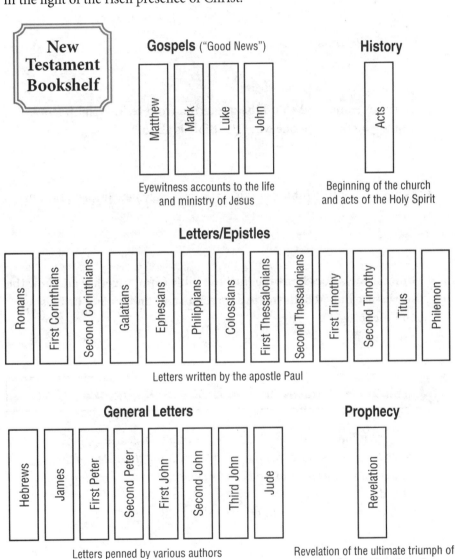

New Testament Bookshelf

Gospels ("Good News")

Matthew, Mark, Luke, John

Eyewitness accounts to the life and ministry of Jesus

History

Acts

Beginning of the church and acts of the Holy Spirit

Letters/Epistles

Romans, First Corinthians, Second Corinthians, Galatians, Ephesians, Philippians, Colossians, First Thessalonians, Second Thessalonians, First Timothy, Second Timothy, Titus, Philemon

Letters written by the apostle Paul

General Letters

Hebrews, James, First Peter, Second Peter, First John, Second John, Third John, Jude

Letters penned by various authors

Prophecy

Revelation

Revelation of the ultimate triumph of Christ, written by John from Patmos

The Bible contains the unfolding story of God's redemptive plan and purposes to save the world—the object of God's love.

1 GROUP DISCUSSION

1. **What is the Bible?**

   a. **Old Testament**

   b. **New Testament**

2. **Have someone read aloud the quotation from N. T. Wright. How would you tell someone what the Bible is about?**

3. **What part of this Bible overview is completely new information to you?**

4. **In what ways does knowing how the Bible is put together and how the stories are linked help you to appreciate and understand its message and meaning?**

2 VIDEO HIGHLIGHTS: THE BIBLE IS INSPIRED BY GOD

Every scripture is inspired by God and is useful for teaching, for showing mistakes, for correcting, and for training character, so that the person who belongs to God can be equipped to do everything that is good.

2 Timothy 3:16-17 CEB

- All Scripture is inspired by God.

- Inspiration means that Scripture is both divine and human—God's words in the language of people.

- The principles of interpretation
  - ○ *Exegesis*—to draw the original meaning out of the text.
    The goal of exegesis is to answer the question *What did the original author really mean, and how would the first audience have understood the meaning?*
  - ○ *Hermeneutics*—the branch of knowledge that deals with interpretation of literary texts, especially of the Bible; our seeking the contemporary relevance and application of the text.
    The goal of hermeneutics is to answer the question *What does the text mean for us today?*

2 GROUP DISCUSSION

1. What does it mean to say that the Bible is *inspired*?

2. Have someone read aloud 2 Timothy 3:16-17 and 2 Peter 1:20-21. What do these verses tell us about the authority of the Bible?

3. Discuss the work of exegesis. How does exegesis help us learn to understand the Scriptures?

4. Discuss the work of hermeneutics. How does applying the Scriptures to our lives and our current context help us to understand them?

5. Why are both exegesis and hermeneutics important for Bible study?

6. Can you think of a contemporary example where Scripture has been misused or misapplied? What were the consequences?

7. Have someone read aloud 2 Timothy 2:15. What is Paul admonishing young Timothy to do? How might we apply this passage to our lives?

3 VIDEO HIGHLIGHTS: THE ENGLISH BIBLE

2000 BC	OT translated from Hebrew to Greek (Septuagaint)
Day of Jesus	OT exists in Hebrew and Greek
Early Chrisitanity	NT written in Koine Greek
Fourth Century	Bible translated into Latin by St. Jerome
1384	First English translation by John Wycliffe
1525	William Tyndale's English Bible
1611	King James Bible
1901	American Standard Bible
1952	Revised Standard Version
1970	New American Standard Bible
Mid 1970's	New International Version
1979	New King James Bible
Today	Many translations and paraphrases available

- All translations are good, but none of them is perfect. So we must become Bible readers, Bible students.

Here I am, I and my Bible. I will not, I dare not ever vary from this book either in great things or in small. I have no power to dispense with one jot or tittle of what is contained therein. I am determined to be a Bible Christian, not almost, but altogether. Who will meet me on this ground? Join me on this or not at all.[2]

—John Wesley

3 GROUP DISCUSSION

1. According to the video, where did our English Bible come from?

2. What were you surprised to learn about how the Bible came to be?

3. Take a look at the different translations of Psalm 23 on page 48. Share your thoughts about how they compare with one another. Did you learn anything new by reading different versions of this familiar passage?

4. Have someone read aloud the quote from John Wesley. Discuss what it might mean to be a "Bible Christian."

5. Discuss some realistic goals for developing your personal Bible study skills. Based on your current Bible study habits, what might your next step be?

Bible Translations of Psalm 23

Common English Bible (CEB)
Psalm 23
A Psalm of David

1 The Lord is my shepherd. I lack nothing.
2 He lets me rest in grassy meadows; he leads me to restful waters;
3 he keeps me alive. He guides me in proper paths for the sake of his good name.
4 Even when I walk through the darkest valley, I fear no danger because you are with me. Your rod and your staff—they protect me.
5 You set a table for me right in front of my enemies. You bathe my head in oil; my cup is so full it spills over!
6 Yes, goodness and faithful love will pursue me all the days of my life, and I will live in the Lord's house as long as I live.

King James Version (KJV)
Psalm 23
A Psalm of David

1 The Lord is my shepherd; I shall not want.
2 He maketh me to lie down in green pastures: he leadeth me beside the still waters.
3 He restoreth my soul: he leadeth me in the paths of righteousness for his name's sake.
4 Yea, though I walk through the valley of the shadow of death, I will fear no evil: for thou art with me; thy rod and thy staff they comfort me.
5 Thou preparest a table before me in the presence of mine enemies: thou anointest my head with oil; my cup runneth over.
6 Surely goodness and mercy shall follow me all the days of my life: and I will dwell in the house of the Lord for ever.

The Message (Message)
Psalm 23
A Psalm of David

1 God, my shepherd! I don't need a thing.
2 You have bedded me down in lush meadows, you find me quiet pools to drink from.
3 True to your word, you let me catch my breath and send me in the right direction.
4 Even when the way goes through Death Valley, I'm not afraid when you walk at my side. Your trusty shepherd's crook makes me feel secure.
5 You serve me a six-course dinner right in front of my enemies. You revive my drooping head; my cup brims with blessing.
6 Your beauty and love chase after me every day of my life. I'm back home in the house of God for the rest of my life.

New International Version (NIV)
Psalm 23
A Psalm of David

1 The Lord is my shepherd, I lack nothing.
2 He makes me lie down in green pastures, he leads me beside quiet waters,
3 he refreshes my soul. He guides me along the right paths for his name's sake.
4 Even though I walk through the darkest valley, I will fear no evil, for you are with me; your rod and your staff, they comfort me.
5 You prepare a table before me in the presence of my enemies. You anoint my head with oil; my cup overflows.
6 Surely your goodness and love will follow me all the days of my life, and I will dwell in the house of the Lord forever.

REVIEW

In this session, the main points were:

1.

2.

3.

What is important about the Bible?

Why is the Bible important to your faith journey as a Christian?

CLOSING

In the last video segment you heard about how an older man who took an introduction to the Bible class was moved to tears when he learned things about the Bible that he had never known before—things that would help him to read and study the Bible. What steps do you need to take to incorporate Bible study into your regular routine?

Check all that apply and plan to move toward these steps this week.

_____ Select and purchase a Bible translation.

_____ Select an individual Bible study resource, reading plan, or journal.

_____ Make space in my daily routine for focused Bible study.

_____ Assess my growth in knowledge of Scripture.

PRAY TOGETHER

Share joys and concerns among your group. Write down anything you are asked to pray for.

Lord God, help us to become men and women of the book. Thank you for the historical witness of your active work in the world. Thank you for the women and men of history who have been inspired by you and have penned your word, as well as those who have given their lives to preserve it. Forgive us for our lackadaisical attitude toward the book we possess, your written revelation. Let today be a new start that we might be men and women of the book, for all Scripture is inspired by you to help us come to know you. In Jesus' name. Amen.

WALKING IT OUT

- Continue the journey by reflecting on the three main ideas of the session throughout the coming week:

  1. The Bible is a compilation of sixty-six books by various authors through which God reveals to us God's nature and covenant love for humanity.

  2. The Bible is the inspired Word of God.

  3. Jesus Christ is God's Living Word and the Bible is the faithful witness to the historical person of Christ as God unfolds God's redemptive work in the world.

- In your personal prayer time:

  ○ give thanks for the Bible, which reveals to us who God is and how much God loves us.

  ○ invite God to speak to you through the Scriptures each time you open your Bible.

  ○ offer praise for the witness of God's love and grace in the Bible.

- Reflect on this question in the coming week: *How are you learning more about God as you seek to understand Scripture?*

- Give more thought to your God story (Before Christ/Choose Christ/ Live for Christ). Review your story (page 23), refining it if you wish, and practice sharing it with others as God provides opportunities.

STUDYING THE SCRIPTURES

Above all, you must understand that no prophecy of Scripture came about by the prophet's own interpretation of things. For prophecy never had its origin in the human will, but prophets, though human, spoke from God as they were carried along by the Holy Spirit.
2 Peter 1:20-21

CORE TRAITS

- Bible Understanding

WELCOME

A core trait of a deeply committed Christian is Bible understanding, and to gain Bible understanding we have to study it and apply it to our lives. Studying the Bible gives us a greater understanding of the nature, purpose, and content of the Old and New Testaments, as well as a general foundation for our faith. In this session you will explore four important tools for Bible study and learn about some basic resources that can help you in your study of God's Word.

CONNECT

Discuss the following questions with your group to get to know one another better and get the conversation started.

- What is one object from your childhood that you no longer have but would love to have back?

- What is one redeeming quality of the person you find most difficult to know? (No names, please.)

- What question would you most like to ask God?

- Last week we learned about the inspiration of Scripture and how our Bible came to be organized. Did this knowledge have any impact on your Bible reading this week? If so, how?

In the space that follows, write down the names of people in your group and one thing about each of them that you learned in conversation. This will help you to remember names and get to know one another a little more.

REFLECT

Assess your current Bible study habits to gauge how often you dig into the Scriptures. Check all that apply to your current routine.

_____ **Daily Bible reading**
_____ **Regular in-depth Bible study**
_____ **Weekly/monthly Scripture verse memorization**
_____ **Bible verses/insights through social media**
_____ **Audio Bible**
_____ **E-devotional**
_____ **Read-through-the-Bible reading plan**
_____ **Other:**

Now, go back and circle the ones that you would like to incorporate into your regular routine.

1 VIDEO HIGHLIGHTS: WHY WE STUDY THE BIBLE

We haven't received the world's spirit but God's Spirit so that we can know the things given to us by God. These are the things we are talking about—not with words taught by human wisdom but with words taught by the Spirit—we are interpreting spiritual things to spiritual people. But people who are unspiritual don't accept the things from God's Spirit. They are foolishness to them and can't be understood, because they can only be comprehended in a spiritual way. Spiritual people comprehend everything, but they themselves aren't understood by anyone. Who has known the mind of the Lord, who will advise him? But we have the mind of Christ.

1 Corinthians 2:12-16 CEB

- When we study Scripture, we can understand it only by means of the Holy Spirit.

  Disclaimer: We can't know everything there is to know about the Bible.

  The secret things belong to the LORD our God. The revealed things belong to us and to our children forever: to keep all the words of this covenant.

Deuteronomy 29:29 CEB

- While we won't ever know everything about the Scriptures, there is still a lot that we can know. God will reveal these things to us through the Holy Spirit if we are listening.

- What is the difference between reading and studying the Bible?

  ○ Reading the Bible is done at our leisure for pleasure and inspiration.

  ○ Study digs a little deeper—with intention.

- Why study the Bible?

  ○ It pleases God. (God desires to be in relationship with us. As we study the Bible, we get to know God better.)

  Make an effort to present yourself to God as a tried-and-true worker, who doesn't need to be ashamed but is one who interprets the message of truth correctly.

2 Timothy 2:15 CEB

  ○ We learn to live and grow as a Christian.

  ○ We develop spiritual discernment and learn to understand what God is saying to us.

  ○ We are able to answer others' questions.

  But in your hearts set apart Christ as Lord. Always be prepared to give an answer to everyone who asks you to give the reason for the hope that you have. But do this with gentleness and respect.

1 Peter 3:15

1 GROUP DISCUSSION

1. **Discuss the difference between reading and studying the Bible.**

2. **Read 1 Corinthians 2:14, 16. By what means does God help us to understand the Bible?**

3. **Have someone read aloud 2 Timothy 2:15 and 1 Peter 3:15. Talk about why it is important for Christians to study the Bible.**

2 VIDEO HIGHLIGHTS: BIBLE STUDY TOOLS

Open my eyes that I may see wonderful things in your law.
Psalm 119:18

Four Important Tools

1. Prayer

- We begin Bible study with *prayer.*
  - ○ When we pray before we study, we invite God to open our hearts and minds and to guide us to the truth of what the Scriptures say.
  - ○ The Holy Spirit communicates through revelation and illumination—revealing meaning and illuminating what it means for our lives.

2. Observation

- What exactly does the text say?
  - ○ Context is of the utmost importance when studying Scripture.
  - ○ When observing Scripture, we need to understand the immediate context, book context, context of other writings by the same author (if available), context of Old or New Testament, context of entire Bible, and historical and cultural context.

- We must understand the context before we can apply the Scriptures to our lives.

- Identify and unpack *word meanings* and *key words*.
  - How are the words being used and what do they mean in the context?
  - Key words show contrast, volume, or comparison.
  - Repetition of words reveals a writer's emphasis.
  - Signal words are "watch out" words to help us understand the context.
  - Expressions of time show us the "when" of the context.

- Focus on the obvious.
  - Author—who is it? Why is the author writing this? What does the author talk about the most?
  - Who? What? When? Where? Why? How?

3. Interpretation

- What does the text mean?
  - Think about what it meant to the original audience. Avoid applying today's tradition to biblical tradition.

- What type of literature is it?
  - Allegory—a symbolic representation
  - Hyperbole—an exaggeration
  - Metaphor—a figure of speech
  - Analogy—a likeness between two ideas
  - Parable—a short, fictitious story that illustrates a moral teaching

4. Application

- How does the meaning of the text apply to me right now in my own situation?

Tools for Study =
Prayer ⇢ Observation ⇢ Interpretation ⇢ Application

"In the beginning God created the heavens and the earth."
Genesis 1:1

Prayer: *God, open my heart and mind and guide me to the truth of what this Scripture says.*

Observation: God created the heavens and the earth.

Interpretation: God was there before the world; God created the world.

Application: God created the world I live in. I believe in a Creator. One God.

Resources for Bible Study

- Concordance: An alphabetical index of key words in the Bible.
- Bible Commentary: A book or document written by a theologian that helps to explain and interpret a particular book or theme of the Bible.
- Bible Atlas: Maps of Bible times.
- Bible Handbook and Dictionary: Bible facts and definitions.

2 | GROUP DISCUSSION

1. Why is prayer an important part of Bible study?

2. What are the key components of observation in Bible study?

3. How do we begin to do the work of interpreting Scripture?

4. **How do we do the work of applying the Scriptures to our lives?**

5. **Use each of the following resources to complete the exercise(s) listed below it:**

Concordance

1. Locate the Scripture that tells how Paul (Saul) escaped the Jews who were plotting to kill him by being lowered in a *basket* through an opening in the city wall.

2. Locate the Scripture that tells how God instructed Moses to strike a *rock* that would produce water for the people to drink.

3. What is another word you might have used to find these same Scriptures?

Bible Commentary

1. Locate Philippians 1 in multiple commentaries. What do the commentaries have in common? How do they differ? Which is most helpful for you? Why?

Bible Atlas

1. Compare a map of Bible lands in Old Testament times with one in New Testament times. What remained the same? What changed? What other useful maps or tools do you find in this atlas?

3 | VIDEO HIGHLIGHTS: BIBLE STUDY PRACTICE

Jesus declared, "I tell you the truth, no one can see the kingdom of God unless he is born again."

John 3:3

Practice

(To be read aloud by the facilitator before the video.)

Now there was a man of the Pharisees named Nicodemus, a member of the Jewish ruling council. He came to Jesus at night and said, "Rabbi, we know you are a teacher who has come from God. For no one could perform the miraculous signs you are doing if God were not with him."

In reply Jesus declared, "I tell you the truth, no one can see the kingdom of God unless he is born again."

"How can a man be born when he is old?" Nicodemus asked. "Surely he cannot enter a second time into his mother's womb to be born!"

Jesus answered, "I tell you the truth, no one can enter the kingdom of God unless he is born of water and the Spirit. Flesh gives birth to flesh, but the Spirit gives birth to spirit. You should not be surprised at my saying, 'You must be born again.' The wind blows wherever it pleases. You hear its sound, but you cannot tell where it comes from or where it is going. So it is with everyone born of the Spirit."

"How can this be?" Nicodemus asked.

"You are Israel's teacher," said Jesus, "and do you not understand these things? I tell you the truth, we speak of what we know, and we testify to what we have seen, but still you people do not accept our testimony. I have spoken to you of earthly things and you do not believe; how then will you believe if I speak of heavenly things? No one has ever gone into heaven except the one who came from heaven—the Son of Man. Just as Moses lifted up the snake in the desert, so the Son of Man must be lifted up, that everyone who believes in him may have eternal life.

"For God so loved the world that he gave his one and only Son, that whoever believes in him shall not perish but have eternal life. For God did not send his Son into the world to condemn the world, but to save the world through him. Whoever believes in him is not condemned, but whoever does not believe stands condemned already because he has not believed in the name of God's one and only Son. This is the verdict: Light has come into the world, but men loved darkness instead of light because their deeds were evil. Everyone who does evil hates the light, and will not come into the light for fear that his deeds will be exposed. But whoever lives by the truth comes into the light, so that it may be seen plainly that what he has done has been done through God."

John 3:1-21

- Who is the author?

- Does the authorship matter in this passage? Why or why not?

- Who are the principal characters?

- What is happening?

- Where are they?

- What time of day is it?

- Who is talking in verse 16 ("For God so loved the world...")? What is so interesting about who is speaking here?

- Who is Jesus saying he is in verse 16?

- What are the key words in this verse?

- What has been done through God according to verse 21 ("But whoever lives by the truth...")? (Hint: Look back at verse 16.)

- What did you learn from John 3:16?

Review

- <u>Author</u>: The author is thought to be John the apostle.

- <u>Significance of authorship</u>: John was very close to Jesus and likely would have learned about this story from Jesus firsthand.

- <u>Principal characters</u>: Nicodemus, Jesus, God, the world

  - Nicodemus—What do we know about him? His name; he's a Pharisee; he's a member of the Jewish ruling counsel (Sanhedrin); he's a man.

  - Look at the margin Scripture references for more information:

    Mark 2:16—"When the teachers of the law who were Pharisees." Pharisees = teachers of the law.

    John 7:50-51—"Nicodemus, who had gone to Jesus earlier and who was one of their own number. " Nicodemus is arguing with Pharisees and sticking up for Jesus.

    Mark 14:55 (AMP)—"Now the chief priests and the entire council (the Sanhedrin) were constantly seeking [to get] testimony against Jesus with a view to condemning Him and putting Him to death, but they did not find any." The Sanhedrin "tried" Jesus. These Jewish rulers held the power, and their livelihood would be taken away if the people believed Jesus; they were responsible for investigating false messiahs.

    John 19:39 (CEB)—"Nicodemus, the one who had first come to Jesus at night, was there too. He brought a mixture of myrrh and aloe, nearly seventy-five pounds in all." Nicodemus went with Joseph of Arimathea in the daylight with a large quantity of spices that would have been expensive and indicates he was a person of wealth. It further suggests he was not afraid or cautious anymore.

- <u>What is happening</u>: Nicodemus goes to find Jesus and talks with him privately.

- <u>Where</u>: Verse 2 tells us that Nicodemus went to where Jesus was. ("He came to Jesus at night.")

- <u>Time of day</u>: Verse 2 indicates that it is night.

- This is the time that rabbis did their studying, so it was the appropriate time.

- Contrast of darkness and light:

    John 3:19—"*Light has come into the world, but men loved darkness instead of light.*"

    John 3:21—"*Whoever lives by the truth comes into the light.*"

- <u>Who is talking in verse 16</u>: Jesus is talking about himself and his role in God's redemption of the world.

- <u>Who Jesus is saying he is</u>: God's Son, the Savior of the world.

- <u>Key words in verse 16</u>: *one, Son, God, loved, gave, world, eternal*

- <u>What has been done through God</u>: Because of love, God has given us God's only Son to bring about the salvation of the world.

- <u>What you learned:</u>

    (Prayer)—Observation, Interpretation, Application

    - Observation: God gave his one Son for us; God initiates salvation.

    - Interpretation: The center of who God is: LOVE.

    - Observation: What's the extent of God's love—what's the measurement? God loved the whole WORLD.

    - Interpretation: God's love encompasses the entire world, but here in this conversation between Jesus and Nicodemus, God's love is also very personal. Saint Augustine said, "God loves each one of us as if there was only one of us to love."[1]

    - Application: The choice—Live in darkness or Light?

3 GROUP DISCUSSION

1. **Describe the experience of studying the story of Jesus and Nicodemus. Were you surprised at all the layers and background information? How?**

2. How do you better understand the love of God after studying this passage from John 3?

3. Discuss what it looks like to live in the darkness in today's world. Then discuss what it looks like to live in the Light.

4. Revisit the idea that Bible study is essential in order to move forward in the journey to know God. How will you make time to study God's Word and seek to know God better?

REVIEW

In this session, the main points were:

1.

2.

3.

What did you discover today about the importance of Bible study in the life of a Christian?

CLOSING

In the last video segment you heard about how intentional Bible study grew Renee's faith in a life-changing way.

List below some things that you hope to get out of Bible study. What do you expect will happen to your knowledge of God, your faith, and your love for God and others as a result of studying the Bible?

Pray Together

Share joys and concerns among your group. Write down anything you are asked to pray for.

God, help us to understand all that we have learned today. Reveal yourself to us when we open up your Word. We ask your Holy Spirit to help us observe, interpret, and apply what we learn from your Word in our lives. It's in your precious name we pray. Amen.

WALKING IT OUT

- Continue the journey by reflecting on the three main ideas of the session throughout the coming week:

  1. We study the Bible because it pleases God, teaches us how to live and grow as a Christian, helps us to develop spiritual discernment, and equips us to answer questions when asked.

  2. We study the Bible using prayer, observation, interpretation, and application.

  3. When we study the Bible we discover the truth about who God is and God's great love for the whole world.

- In your personal prayer time,

  - give thanks that God desires to be in relationship with you. Tell God that you want to know God more by studying God's Word.

  - ask the Holy Spirit to reveal the meaning of the Scriptures as you open up the Bible.

  - praise God for the gift of the Bible. Thank God for giving us such a special witness to God's great love for us.

- As you learn to study the Bible and begin to understand the Scriptures more fully, pay attention to testimonies of great Bible characters and see what God was able to do through them because of their obedience.

- Give more thought to your own God story (Before Christ/Choose Christ/Live for Christ). Review your story (page 23), refining it if you wish, and practice sharing it with others as God provides opportunities.

A STUDY OF CHRISTIAN ETHICS

Jesus replied: "'Love the Lord your God with all your heart and with all your soul and with all your mind.' This is the first and greatest commandment. And the second is like it: 'Love your neighbor as yourself.' All the Law and the Prophets hang on these two commandments."

Matthew 22:37-40

CORE TRAITS

- Christian Ethics

- Knowing God's Will

WELCOME

When we talk about *ethics*, we are referring to a system of moral principles or values. So what do we mean when we talk about *Christian ethics*? Christian ethics is defined as the systematic study of the way of life set forth by Jesus Christ applied to the daily demands and decisions of human existence. In this session you will consider how knowing God requires an understanding of God's will—based on study of the Bible and the life and teachings of Jesus—in order to apply Christian principles to the problems and decisions we face in life.

CONNECT

Discuss the following questions with your group to get to know one another better and get the conversation started.

- If you could become a famous athlete for a season, who would you be?

- What do you think makes a house a home?

- Last week you were introduced to some new tools to aid in your study of Scripture. Share which of these tools you utilized in the previous week. What did you learn?

In the space that follows, write the names of people in your group and one thing about each of them that you learned in conversation. This will help you remember names and get to know one another a little more.

REFLECT

What do you think of when you hear the word *ethics*? Write a definition of the word in your own words.

1 VIDEO HIGHLIGHTS: WHAT IS CHRISTIAN ETHICS?

"[God] has shown all you people what is good. And what does the LORD require of you? To act justly and to love mercy and to walk humbly with your God."
                    Micah 6:8 TNIV

- In previous sessions we have learned that
    - we know God through a growing, personal relationship; through the life, teachings, and ministry of Jesus Christ; and through the inspired Word of God; and

> **Christian ethics** – "The systematic study of the way of life set forth by Jesus Christ applied to the daily demands and decisions of our personal and social existence."

- The Role of Scripture in Ethics

  - The Bible doesn't cover every situation that we're going to face throughout our lives.

  - The Bible is the central influence on the life of the Christian.

  - The Bible is always primary but rarely self-sufficient; it gives us the basis but not the exact application. We have to dig deeper.

- Old Testament: The narrative of God's relationship with God's chosen people. God would redeem his people.

"I'm declaring war between you and the Woman,
between your offspring and hers.
He'll wound your head,
you'll wound his heel."
Genesis 3:15 The Message

  - God cares about the conduct of his people—not for the sake of rules and laws, but in desire for them to have a good life and be healthy and protected.

  - God cares deeply about social justice.

[God] has shown all you people what is good.
*   And what does the* LORD *require of you?*
To act justly and to love mercy
*   and to walk humbly with your God.*
Micah 6:8 TNIV

To walk humbly with God is to know him intimately and to be attentive to what he desires and loves.[1]
—Timothy Keller

- *Mercy* comes from the Hebrew word *khesedh* (hesed) and refers to God's unconditional grace and compassion.

- The Hebrew word for justice is *mishpat* (occurs in the Old Testament more than two hundred times).

- Together, these two imply attitude and action. *Khesedh* provides the motivation for *mishpat*, or action.

- God desires that all classes and races of people be treated with *khesedh* and *mishpat*.

- <u>New Testament</u>: The basis for Christian ethics is most clearly seen in the Gospels—in the life, teachings, and ministry of Jesus.

  Make the Master proud of you by being good citizens. Respect the authorities, whatever their level; they are God's emissaries for keeping order. It is God's will that by doing good, you might cure the ignorance of the fools who think you're a danger to society. Exercise your freedom by serving God, not by breaking the rules. Treat everyone you meet with dignity. Love your spiritual family. Revere God. Respect the government.
  1 Peter 2:13-17 *The Message*

  Remind the people to be subject to rulers and authorities, to be obedient, to be ready to do whatever is good.
  Titus 3:1 TNIV

- How to discern ethical behavior based on Scripture:

  - Rely on God

  - Search for biblical principles

  - Pray over God's word

  - Seek the guidance of the Holy Spirit

- Cautions

  - Be sure to apply everything you have learned in previous sessions about context, interpretation, and application when you seek the Bible for answers to ethical dilemmas.

  - Don't misuse Scripture to back up your opinion.

1 GROUP DISCUSSION

1. When have you found yourself in an ethical dilemma—a time when you were perplexed or troubled about how to apply Christian principles to a problem or decision you faced? How did you figure out what to do? What happened?

2. Do you think the Bible is helpful for working through ethical problems? Why or why not?

3. What are some ways that people sometimes misuse Scripture to back up their opinions?

4. What do you think are the major ethical dilemmas of our time? How might searching the Scriptures give us insight as we form opinions and behaviors about these issues?

5. How is Micah 6:8 a definition of Christian ethics?

2 VIDEO HIGHLIGHTS: CHRISTIAN ETHICS IN THE GOSPELS

"'Love the Lord your God with all your heart and with all your soul and with all your mind.' This is the first and greatest commandment. And the second is like it: 'Love your neighbor as yourself.' All the Law and the Prophets hang on these two commandments."
Matthew 22:37-40

1. Jesus taught an ethic that was completely integrated with his faith: love of God, love for neighbor and self.

- There's a connection between the Spirit working through Jesus by virtue of his anointing and the mission of Jesus' life.

"The Spirit of the Lord is on me,
because he has anointed me
to proclaim good news to the poor.
He has sent me to proclaim freedom for the prisoners
and recovery of sight for the blind,
to set the oppressed free,
to proclaim the year of the Lord's favor."
Luke 4:18-19 TNIV

- In the Sermon on the Mount, Jesus said . . .

  ○ "Love your enemies . . . that you may be children of your Father in heaven" (Matthew 5:44-45).

  ○ "Blessed are the peacemakers,
    for they will be called children of God" (Matthew 5:9).

  ○ "Be perfect . . . as your heavenly Father is perfect" (Matthew 5:48).

  ○ "Be merciful, just as your Father is merciful" (Luke 6:36).

2. Jesus stressed how our inward spiritual state relates to our outward actions.

"You're hopeless, you religion scholars and Pharisees! Frauds! You keep meticulous account books, tithing on every nickel and dime you get, but on the meat of God's Law, things like fairness and compassion and commitment—the absolute basics!—you carelessly take it or leave it. Careful bookkeeping is commendable, but the basics are required. Do you have any idea how silly you look, writing a life story that's wrong from start to finish, nitpicking over commas and semicolons?

"You're hopeless, you religion scholars and Pharisees! Frauds! You burnish the surface of your cups and bowls so they sparkle in the sun, while the insides are maggoty with your greed and gluttony. Stupid Pharisee! Scour the insides, and then the gleaming surface will mean something."
Matthew 23:23-26 *The Message*

- Timothy Keller summarizes theologian Jonathan Edwards' argument, "human beings will only be drawn out of themselves into unselfish acts of service to others when they see God as supremely beautiful."[2]

- *If you listen to the music of Bach because you want people to think you are cultured... then the music is only a means to acheive some other end, namely the enhancement of your reputation. But if you play Bach because you find it just not useful but beautiful, then you are listening to it as satisfying in and of itself.*[3]

  —Timothy Keller

- In Jesus we see a shift away from legalism and self-interest toward those inner attitudes that determine the nature and motive of our actions.

- Jesus lived a God-centered life—one of love, faith, purity of heart, compassion, honesty in speech, and a self-giving attitude.

3. Jesus declared the worth of every person; he saw people through the eyes of God.

   - If we truly see people as God sees people, it will influence our actions.

2 GROUP DISCUSSION

1. **Have someone read aloud Luke 4:18-19. According to this passage, how does Jesus describe his mission?**

2. **Skim the Sermon on the Mount (Matthew 5–7), and look for and list the teachings that demonstrate a joining of faith and action.**

3. **Why does inner motivation matter to Jesus?**

4. **Have someone read Matthew 23:23-26. What does it mean to "scour the insides" so that "the gleaming surface will mean something" (v. 26 *The Message*)?**

5. Discuss the idea of legalism. What are some examples of legalism today?

6. What can help us begin to see people as Jesus sees them?

3   VIDEO HIGHLIGHTS: CHRISTIAN ETHICS IN ACTION

"'Love the Lord your God with all your heart and with all your soul and with all your mind and with all your strength.' The second is this: 'Love your neighbor as yourself.' There is no commandment greater than these."

Mark 12:30-31

Love God. Love self. Love neighbor.

- Love God

  ○ Seek after God's kingdom as a treasure.

  "But seek first his kingdom and his righteousness, and all these things will be given to you as well."
  Matthew 6:33 NIV

  ○ Look to God first. Trust that God desires the best for us.

  "What I'm trying to do here is get you to relax, not be so preoccupied with getting so you can respond to God's giving. People who don't know God and the way he works fuss over these things, but you know both God and how he works. Steep yourself in God-reality, God-initiative, God-provisions. You'll find all your everyday human concerns will be met. Don't be afraid of missing out. You're my dearest friends! The Father wants to give you the very kingdom itself."
  Luke 12:29-32 *The Message*

- Love Self

  ○ Trust God to equip you, through the Holy Spirit, for every situation, and allow God's love and light to shine through you.

- ○ Take good care of yourself. This includes:
  - * respecting yourself,
  - * avoiding harmful things,
  - * caring for your health,
  - * pursuing education,
  - * preparing to do your best work,
  - * engaging in meaningful work,
  - * enjoying fruitful time of leisure,
  - * cultivating wholesome family life, and
  - * acquiring enough material goods.
- ○ Fit yourself for service—become the best you can be to be used by God.

- Love Neighbor
  - ○ Public face versus private face—who I am when I'm out in the community versus who I am when I'm at home or alone.
  - ○ Duty to Society
    - * We are called to seek justice, to care for the poor, and to be involved in social service, education, economics, and politics.
    - * In every social decision there is an *ideally right course, a best possible course*, and *the course we are tempted to take* because it is easy or in conformity with the standard of our culture.
    - * There are no easy answers to many of the complex social issues of our day, but God is calling us to do what is ours to do.

- Christian Ethics in the everyday
  - ○ We must apply Christian ethics to everyday decisions—to the mundane, day-in-day-out stuff of life.
  - ○ To paraphrase Georgia Harkness, the greater good is that choice that reflects the fullest embodiment of God-centered faith and love. God will always guide us when making important decisions in life.[4]

3 | GROUP DISCUSSION

1. Have someone read aloud Ephesians 4:1-2; 3 John 1:2; 1 Corinthians 3:16; and 1 Corinthians 13:4-7. How do these passages help in your understanding of the perspective and motive of the Christian in the area of love for self? What are the differences between healthy self-love and self-centeredness?

2. Have someone read aloud Romans 12:2. What does this verse have to say about our response to the situations of social sin or evil we find in society? What is the "good, pleasing and perfect" will of God?

3. Have someone read aloud Romans 12:9-21 in several Bible translations, including *The Message*. Do you see this passage as something that is attainable? Why or why not? How might our world look if we took these words to heart? How might our personal lives look if we took these words to heart?

4. Share two or three tangible ways you can express love of God, love of self, and love of neighbor. Make a commitment to put one of the ways discussed into action in the coming week.

REVIEW

In this session, the main point was:

How does exploring Christian ethics help us to know God more?

Why is connecting faith and action important for us as Christians?

Closing

In the last video segment you heard about an ethical dilemma that changed Mike's life.

How does your daily life begin to change when you pay attention to your ethical behavior in the everyday stuff of life?

How might your God-story grow because of a move toward intentional ethical behavior—in the small stuff and the big stuff?

Pray Together

Share joys and concerns among your group. Write down anything you are asked to pray for.

God, thank you for calling us into a relationship with you. Thank you that we can come to know you more personally and intimately through your Word and through Jesus Christ. Teach and guide us by the power of your Holy Spirit to know where our faith intersects with who we are and how we live our lives. At the end of the day, we want to be found loving, just as you were loving; concerned, just as you were concerned. Empower us to be vessels of your love with every person we meet. In Christ's name we pray. Amen.

WALKING IT OUT

- Continue the journey by reflecting on the theme of the session throughout the coming week:

  Knowing God requires an understanding of God's will, based on study of the Bible and the life and teachings of Jesus, in order to apply Christian principles to the problems and decisions of human existence.

- In your personal prayer time:
  - give thanks to God for loving you and wanting good for you;
  - ask the Holy Spirit to equip you to put your faith in action when it comes to Christian ethics;
  - offer praise for the teachings of Jesus and for God's constant presence and grace every step of the way.

- Reflect this week on the following questions: How has your commitment to ethical behavior deepened because you have chosen to follow Jesus Christ? What has changed about your interactions with strangers? with your family? on the highway? at the office?

- Give more thought to your God story (Before Christ/Choose Christ/Live for Christ). Review your story (page 23), refining it if you wish, and practice sharing it with others as God provides opportunities. Remember, people will learn about your faith through your actions. Prepare for sharing your story with the group next week.

THE PERSON AND WORK OF THE HOLY SPIRIT

I have not stopped giving thanks for you, remembering you in my prayers. I keep asking that the God of our Lord Jesus Christ, the glorious Father, may give you the Spirit of wisdom and revelation, so that you may know him better.

Ephesians 1:16-17

CORE TRAITS

- Christian Essentials
- Church/Denomination
- Knowing God's Will

WELCOME

God does not mean for us to grow in faith and do His work by ourselves. In this session you will discover who the Holy Spirit is and how the Spirit works in and through God's people, the church. Invite God to open your mind and heart and teach you today about the work of the Holy Spirit in the lives of believers.

CONNECT

Discuss the following questions with your group to get to know one another better and get the conversation started.

- If you could be an expert in one subject, which subject would you choose?
- If you had the opportunity to work as an assistant for an entire year for anyone of your choice, whom would you choose?
- Do you think work is valuable for its own sake? Why or why not?
- What is your understanding of the Holy Spirit?
- Why do you think the Holy Spirit is often ignored or misunderstood?

In the space that follows, write the names of people in your group and one thing about each of them that you learned in conversation. Do you feel that you know one another better now than when the study began?

REFLECT

What comes to mind when you think of the Holy Spirit? Make a list of some words that convey your thoughts:

1 VIDEO HIGHLIGHTS: THE BIBLE AND THE HOLY SPIRIT

I keep asking that the God of our Lord Jesus Christ, the glorious Father, may give you the Spirit of wisdom and revelation, so that you may know him better.

Ephesians 1:17

The way we get to know God in a relationship is through the saving activity and power of the Holy Spirit.

Who Is the Holy Spirit?

- The Holy Spirit is God's personal, active presence at work in the world.

- The Hebrew word for God's spirit is *ruakh*, which bears the idea of wind, breath, life-giving energy, and power.

The Holy Spirit in the Old Testament

- The Holy Spirit was prominent in the act of creation. (See Genesis 1:2; 2:7.)

- The Holy Spirit was active in God's work in the world throughout the old covenant.

- The Holy Spirit came upon particular people at particular times in order to empower them for particular tasks. (See Exodus 31:1-5; Judges 6:34; 1 Samuel 16:13; Isaiah 61:1-3.)

- The Old Testament builds anticipation for the coming of a new covenant through which the Holy Spirit would come upon everyone—not just prophets, priests, and favored ones.

> *"This is the covenant I will make with the house of Israel*
> *   after that time," declares the LORD.*
> *"I will put my law in their minds*
> *   and write it on their hearts.*
> *I will be their God,*
> *   and they will be my people."*
>   Jeremiah 31:33

> *"And afterward,*
> *   I will pour out my Spirit on all people.*
> *Your sons and daughters will prophesy,*
> *   your old men will dream dreams,*
> *   your young men will see visions."*
>   Joel 2:28

The Holy Spirit in the New Testament and Beyond

- The Gospels ascribe the source of Jesus' human life to the Holy Spirit (Matthew 1:18; Luke 1:35).

- The Holy Spirit descended upon Jesus at his baptism (Luke 3:21-22).

- Jesus understood his life and ministry as the fulfillment of Isaiah's prophecy (Luke 4:17-21).

- Jesus taught extensively about the Holy Spirit. In John 14–16, Jesus prepared the disciples for the Holy Spirit to come and continue God's work through them. Jesus was anticipating that there would be a new era of God's work in the world and that it would be done through the power of the Holy Spirit.

- After Jesus ascended into heaven, the Holy Spirit came on the day of Pentecost to dwell in all believers. Believers, from that time to now, are people of the new covenant carrying on Jesus' mission.

- We are living in the era of the Holy Spirit. The outpouring of the Holy Spirit, the reception of the Holy Spirit in the life of a Christian, and the work of the Holy Spirit in the moral and spiritual transformation of our lives are the unique aspects of the experiential side of our faith.

1 GROUP DISCUSSION

1. Who is the Holy Spirit? Explain in your own words.

2. Read Acts 2:1-7. How did the Holy Spirit show up in a powerful way?

3. What did you learn from the video that helped you better understand the Holy Spirit?

4. Why do you think the Holy Spirit is one of the least talked about aspects of the Christian faith?

5. How would you summarize the work of the Holy Spirit in the Old Testament?

6. **How would you summarize the work of the Holy Spirit in the New Testament?**

7. **Skim John 14–16 for references to the Holy Spirit. What does Jesus tell his disciples about who the Holy Spirit is and what the Holy Spirit will come to do?**

2 | VIDEO HIGHLIGHTS: THE WORK OF THE HOLY SPIRIT

May the God of hope fill you with all joy and peace in faith so that you overflow with hope by the power of the Holy Spirit.
Romans 15:13 CEB

- **The Holy Spirit draws us to God.**

  - The Holy Spirit is involved in drawing us to God even before our conversion.

  - There are a number of ways that God, by the Holy Spirit, draws us to himself—the Bible, other books, speakers, testimonies, the prayers of others, and so forth.

- **The Holy Spirit gives us new birth.**

  - Nicodemus asks Jesus how to enter God's kingdom. Jesus tells him to be born anew, by the Spirit.

  - The Holy Spirit comes into our lives in what Jesus called "the new birth"—a transformation of our identity.

  - The Holy Spirit is the giver of new spiritual life.

  - The in-dwelling Holy Spirit who comes to live inside helps us to be made new.

- **The Holy Spirit helps us to know God.**

  - When we receive the Holy Spirit, we receive the Spirit of adoption and become children of God.

    All who are led by God's Spirit are God's sons and daughters. You didn't receive a spirit of slavery to lead you back again into fear, but you received a Spirit that shows you are adopted as

*his children. With this Spirit, we cry, "Abba, Father." The same
Spirit agrees with our spirit, that we are God's children.*
Romans 8:14-16 CEB

○ The Holy Spirit helps us to know God better through an ongoing, deepening relationship with Christ.

*I keep asking that the God of our Lord Jesus Christ, the glorious
Father, may give you the Spirit of wisdom and revelation, so
that you may know him better.*
Ephesians 1:17 TNIV

- **The Holy Spirit empowers our Christian witness.**

  ○ The Holy Spirit gives power in witness. The primary work of the Holy Spirit is the empowerment of the church for the proclamation of the gospel.

  *"But you will receive power when the Holy Spirit comes on you;
  and you will be my witnesses in Jerusalem, and in all Judea and
  Samaria, and to the ends of the earth."*
  Acts 1:8

  ○ The Holy Spirit gives strength and courage in the face of adversity (Acts 4:8-22).

  ○ The Holy Spirit causes the church to grow (Acts 2:14-21, 38-41).

- **The Holy Spirit helps us to pray.**

  *The Spirit comes to help our weakness. We don't know what we
  should pray, but the Spirit himself pleads our case with unexpressed
  groans. The one who searches hearts knows how the Spirit thinks,
  because he pleads for the saints, consistent with God's will.*
  Romans 8:26-27 CEB

- **The Holy Spirit continues to transform us.**

  ○ The Holy Spirit is the agent of transformation. The Apostle Paul wrote:

  *The Lord is the Spirit, and where the Lord's Spirit is, there is
  freedom. All of us are looking with unveiled faces at the glory of
  the Lord as if we were looking in a mirror. We are being transformed into that same image from one degree of glory to the
  next degree of glory. This comes from the Lord, who is the Spirit.*
  2 Corinthians 3:17-18 CEB

* This process of transformation is the work of the Holy Spirit; it is not anything we can do by ourselves.

* This transformational power enables us to become like Christ.

○ The Holy Spirit empowers us to live out God's moral code.

2   GROUP DISCUSSION

1. What are some ways that God, by the Holy Spirit, draws us to himself? What are some ways you have been drawn to God?

2. What does it mean to say that the Holy Spirit gives us new birth? How have you been made new, and what does this rebirth mean to you?

3. Have someone read aloud Romans 8:14-17. What does this passage mean to you personally? What difference does knowing that you are a child of God and a coheir with Christ make in your life?

4. What are some ways that the Holy Spirit empowers our Christian witness? How have you been empowered by the Holy Spirit in your own life?

5. What does it mean to say that the Holy Spirit helps us to pray? How does knowing this encourage you?

6. Why is it important for us to understand that transformation is the work of the Holy Spirit?

3   VIDEO HIGHLIGHTS: THE EVIDENCE OF THE HOLY SPIRIT

*But the fruit of the Spirit is love, joy, peace, patience, kindness, good-
ness, faithfulness, gentleness and self-control. Against such things
there is no law.*

Galatians 5:22-23

Evidence of the Holy Spirit includes:

1. the presence and power of God in the individual Christian and the
   Christian community;

2. the spreading of the gospel and God's kingdom work in the world
   through the body of Christ, the church;

3. personal and corporate transformation—a changed life and a changed
   world;

4. the fruit of the Spirit: love, joy, peace, patience, kindness, goodness,
   faithfulness, gentleness, self-control.

- Signs of God's presence, power, and kingdom work include:

    o healing where there was brokenness,

    o hope where there was despair,

    o freedom where there was bondage,

    o forgiveness where there was bitterness,

    o strength where there was weakness,

    o faith where there was uncertainty,

    o peace where there was turmoil,

    o joy where there was sadness, and

    o love where there was indifference or hate.

- The letters of Paul teach us that the Holy Spirit is the transformer of our
  lives and the inner motivation for life change.

*The Lord is the Spirit, and where the Lord's Spirit is, there is freedom.
All of us are looking with unveiled faces at the glory of the Lord as
if we were looking in a mirror. We are being transformed into that*

same image from one degree of glory to the next degree of glory. This comes from the Lord, who is the Spirit.
2 Corinthians 3:17-18 CEB

- ○ The Greek verb for *transformed* means "to be metamorphosized."

- ○ As we behold Christ, we begin to look like him, first inwardly and then outwardly in the way that we live.

- One of the ways we detect this life change is the fruit of the Spirit. As the Spirit changes us from the inside out, we see the fruit in our lives: love, joy, peace, patience, kindness, goodness, faithfulness, gentleness, and self-control.

- What does it look like when we are Spirit filled?

Speak to one another with psalms, hymns and spiritual songs ... always giving thanks to God the Father for everything.
Ephesians 5:19-20 NIV

3 GROUP DISCUSSION

1. **In light of today's teaching, what or who do you now understand the Holy Spirit to be?**

2. **How can we cooperate with the work of the Holy Spirit in our lives? What things might cause the Holy Spirit's work to be impeded? See Ephesians 1:17-19 for insight.**

3. **Have someone read aloud 2 Corinthians 3:17-18. In what ways do you see evidence in our world that we, as the universal church, are being transformed into the likeness of Christ? In what ways do you see evidence of this transformation in your personal life?**

4. **Have someone read aloud 2 Corinthians 3:1-3. If we are indeed a "letter" from Christ, written by the Holy Spirit, who do you think is**

the letter's recipient? How might these thoughts challenge or change your thoughts and actions?

Study Summary

This is eternal life: that the world might know God through his son whom he sent.

John 17:3, author's paraphrase

Review

In this session, the main points were:

1.

2.

3.

When have you felt energized and empowered by the work of the Holy Spirit?

Closing

In the last video segment you heard about how one man experienced transformation after an encounter with the Holy Spirit. Think about the times when you have felt God's presence especially close to you, or a time when you met God in a powerful, life-changing way.

How does the work of the Holy Spirit change your life for the better?

How can you add these thoughts to your story in a compelling way for others to hear and come to know the God you love? If you feel comfortable, share your story with your group.

PRAY TOGETHER

Share joys and concerns among your group. Write down anything you are asked to pray for.

O God, thank you for coming into our world of brokenness, darkness, difficulty, and pain. We are so glad that you initiated coming into the world to save us and help us. We thank you that the word gospel still means good news, and that you have good news for us. I pray that each of us would experience a deepening relationship with you, that the eyes of our hearts might be enlightened, that together, with all of your people, we might come to know how wide and deep and broad is your love for us, and that we might be filled to fullness with the love of Christ. Thank you for the gift of life and the gift of new life through Jesus Christ by the power of the Holy Spirit. Continue the work of inner transformation, filling us with the Holy Spirit so that your word might be living and active in us. In Jesus' name we pray. Amen.

WALKING IT OUT

- Continue the journey by reflecting on the themes of the session throughout the coming week:

  1. The Bible teaches us about the Holy Spirit. Through Old and New Testament Scriptures, we learn who the Holy Spirit is, and about the work and evidence of the Holy Spirit.

  2. The work of the Holy Spirit is to draw us to God, give us new birth and identity, help us to know God, empower us to share our faith and serve, and transform our lives.

  3. We see evidence of the work of the Holy Spirit in our lives:

     - We experience the power of the Spirit working through us as we serve God.

     - The fruit of the Spirit is cultivated in us.

     - We are transformed more and more into the image of Christ.

- In your personal prayer time:

  - give thanks to God for the gift and work of the Holy Spirit;

  - ask the Holy Spirit to equip and empower you to do what God calls you to do; and

  - offer praise for God's great work in and through your life.

- Throughout this study you have been reviewing, refining, and sharing your God-story, how you came to know, love, and follow Jesus. In this last session, you had the opportunity to share your story with your group. In the weeks to come, work on committing your story to memory so that it will come to mind easily whenever the time is right to share it. Pray always for the courage and wisdom to speak freely about what knowing God means to you.

NOTES

Session 1: Receiving Christ

1. Timothy Keller, *The Reason for God: Belief in an Age of Skepticism* (New York: Dutton, 2008), 160.

2. Augustine, *Confessions*, 1.1.1.

Session 2: Comprehending Christ's Teachings

1. Augustine, *Confessions*, 4.14.21.

2. Ronald Youngblood, ed., "Parable," Nelson's New Illustrated Bible Dictionary, (Nashville:Thomas Nelson, 2005), 943.

Session 3: Learning the Scriptures

1. N. T. Wright, *Simply Christian: Why Christianity Makes Sense* (HarperSanFrancisco, 2006), 73.

2. John Wesley, "Causes of the Inefficacy of Christianity." John Wesley's Sermons: An Anthology (Nashville: Abingdon, 1991), 549.

Session 4: Studying the Scriptures

1. William Barclay, *The Gospel of John*, The New Daily Study Bible (Louisville: Westminster/John Knox, 2001), 1:161.

Session 5: A Study of Christian Ethics

1. Timothy Keller, *Generous Justice: How God's Grace Makes Us Just* (New York: Riverhead, 2012), 3.

2. Timothy Keller, *Generous Justice*, 182.

3. Timothy Keller, *Generous Justice*, 182-3.

4. Georgia Harkness, "Christian Ethics," http://www.religion-online.org/showchapter.asp?title=802&c=1078.

Each of the Journey 101 authors is on staff at The United Methodist Church of the Resurrection in Leawood, Kansas, where they developed, wrote, and implemented *Journey 101* as the basic discipleship course for their congregation of more than 15,000 members. The program has since spread to many churches beyond their home church and denomination.

Carol Cartmill is Executive Director of Adult Discipleship.
Jeff Kirby is Minister of Adult Discipleship and Men's Ministry.
Michelle Kirby is Learning Events Program Director.